Sparkle, Spirit, Style!

It's Great to Be an American Girl!

To appear on the cover, place your picture here.

W9-CTS-294

This book is just for you—and your new doll, too.

Play the "I Like Your Style!" CD. Turn the pages of this book and sing along! Find words of encouragement taken from our many other American Girl books, too. You'll discover that style is much more than the clothes you wear or the way you do your hair. True style is all about a mix of your interests, your heart, and your spirit. It's about what's inside you!

Then, turn to the second section of this book, give your doll a name, and s-t-r-e-t-c-h your imagination to create her special style.

Have fun!

Your friends at American Girl

Look in back for the "I Like Your Style!" music CD.

You have a unique voice. In fact, nobody else in the world has your voice. So, how do you find your voice? Where is it hiding? . . . Look in your heart. And in your head.

—*Writing Smarts*

Wow! I want to be singing, My life is sure feeling great!

Making new friends is easier when you have something in common to share. Join after-school clubs or activities like the school newspaper or the softball team.

—*School Smarts*

'Cause I **learned** something new, Made a **friend** or two—

It's your head, your heart, and your spirit, too, that add up to make YOU.
—*The Care & Keeping of You*

And that is something to celebrate!

You can't control the world. But you can control how you deal with it.
You can learn. You can be smart. You can trust your confidence and your
common sense.

—A Smart Girl's Guide to Sticky Situations

See my
sparkle,
My spirit,
My own kind
of style!

Psst!
Smile. If you feel good
about yourself, others
will too!
—*School Smarts*

Inside me
I feel it
And I want
to smile!

Get involved in charitable giving, and it's hard to go wrong. Doing good feels good. And you'll be helping to create a better, healthier, more peaceful world for everyone, including you. What better way to use money could there be?

—*A Smart Girl's Guide to Money*

Make a time capsule to open together in five or ten years. Write down your dreams and your predictions for the future. Include a description of life as you know it. Put in letters from parents or friends, ticket stubs, and anything else that's important to you today. Seal it up and store it in a safe place!

—*Friends*

Look how much

I love living

At this moment

in time—

In place of gifts (at your party), ask guests to bring dog food for the Humane Society, toys for a local children's center, or canned goods for a food pantry. Activities might be to make crafts or baked goods to sell as a fund-raiser for the cause.

—*Snooze-a-Palooza!*

I can

I can

Physical activity helps make your bones, heart, and muscles stronger. Being active also helps to reduce stress, boost self-confidence, and improve thinking ability.

—*Real Fitness*

I can
shout,
I can
share,

Making good choices starts with using your own best judgment. Take the time to think things through, and you won't go wrong.

—*Staying Home Alone*

And
so many
other
choices
are mine.

Don't waste time comparing yourself to others. There's no one out there just like you, who has grown up with your experiences and has your talents.

—*Real Beauty*

You know, because

we're all different,

Imagine what
it would be

Whether you're a superstar or just out for fun, sports teach you more than how to play a game. You learn lessons about friendship, teamwork, goal setting, and effort.

—*Sports Secrets and Spirit Stuff*

If we each took
a dream,
Went to work as
a team

A goal is what you decide to make happen this week, this month, or this year. Think about what you can do in the near future to make that dream come true.

—*You Can Do It!*

To make a
future full
of promise—
For you and me!

Give yourself a break. No-body's perfect. Don't beat yourself up over every little mistake. Instead, celebrate what you did right, accept and understand what you did wrong, then move on, knowing that you did the best you could do.
—*A Smart Girl's Guide to Starting Middle School*

I like your
sparkle,
Your spirit,
Your own special
style!

A smile is an invitation you wear on your face. It says, "I'm a girl you want to know!"

—*The Care & Keeping of You*

Inside you, you feel it And you want to smile!

You don't have to be an Olympic athlete to be healthy. Just put down that video game, get off that couch, and get moving! Rollerblade to a friend's house or dance to your favorite music. The busier you keep your body, the better you'll feel.

—*The Care &*
Keeping of You

When you face a challenge, tell yourself you are strong and smart. Confidence in yourself will help you keep your cool.

Try to step back and look at the big picture. Change is going to happen, but you'll be able to handle it with real spirit.

—*Real Spirit*

As time goes by I know
that things will be
changing.
I wonder what
I will see?

If the state of the world is stressing you out, do something about it! Write a letter to your principal, your mayor, or even the president. Volunteer your time to a good cause. Helping others will help you feel better, too.

—*Real Spirit*

I'll make
my way,
Say what I have
to say,

People love to hear the sound of their own names. So when you're talking to someone, be sure to drop her name into the conversation every once in a while. To help remember a new name when you first meet someone, use it almost immediately—"Nice to meet you, CLAIRE."

—*Girl Talk*

Trying every day
to be
the best
I can be!

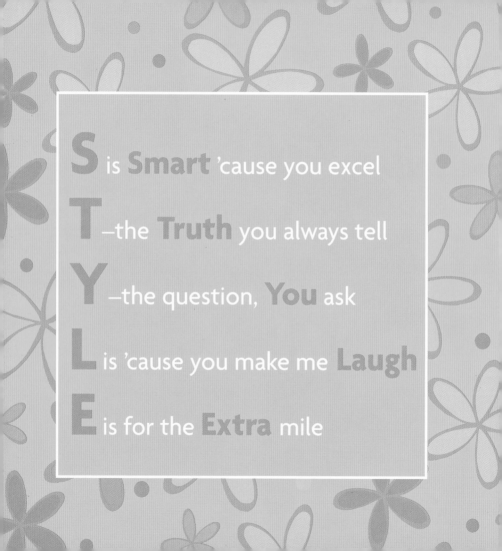

S is **Smart** 'cause you excel

T —the **Truth** you always tell

Y —the question, **You** ask

L is 'cause you make me **Laugh**

E is for the **Extra** mile

Put it all
together, girl,
I like your style—
I like your
style!

When it comes to nature, a girl should enjoy it without leaving a trace that she was ever there.

—*A Smart Girl's Guide to Manners*

There's a kind
of a **world**
where I want
to **live,**

Teach your mother, your little brother, or a friend one of your special skills. It feels good to be an expert! Be patient and give your pupil lots of encouragement. Remember what it was like when you were first learning?
—*Real Beauty*

And there's lots of good inside of me
I'm ready to give!

A best friend can be as comforting as a cup of hot cocoa on a cold winter's night. She listens, she keeps your secrets, and when you're together, it just feels right. You feel safe and secure knowing she's there for you when you need her.

—*A Smart Girl's Guide to Friendship Troubles*

I want to
fill it up with

and

You're never too little to dream big dreams.
—*Coconut's Guide to Life*

I'm glad
to be an
American girl!

You can make your room look almost like new simply by getting rid of things you don't want or use anymore. A clean room is like a fresh start. Lose the clutter and clear your mind. You might even sleep better if your room is neat and tidy.

—*Room Crafts*

'Cause it's our
sparkle,
Our spirit,
Our own kind
of style!

Being friends is like riding a bicycle. Sometimes the ride feels smooth and easy, but other times, you hit bumps in the road. You have to steer carefully and pedal hard to make sure that you stay on the right path. But in the end, friendship is usually worth the ride.

—*Friends*

Inside us, we feel it
And we want
to smile!

Think back to other times in your life when you successfully navigated a new situation (like your first day at gymnastics, summer camp, or swim lessons). Then remind yourself, "Come to think of it, I CAN do this!"
—*A Smart Girl's Guide to Starting Middle School*

Hey! Hey! Hey!

It's so easy to see
It's great
to be an
American girl!

Friends Forever!

If you'd like, place a picture of you and your doll here.

Think about what it's like when you meet a new friend. You wonder if she prefers pizza or pasta, movies or music— even pink or green! But after you ask a lot of questions, you know more about your friend, and your relationship feels really special. Fill in the blanks on the next pages to help shape your American Girl doll's special style.

The Basics

Her full name

_____

She is _____ years old.

She joined our family on

_____

The special occasion was

_____

_____

_____

Her Favorites

color _____

song _____

number _____

ice cream flavor _____

school subject _____

season _____

game _____

sport _____

movie _____

book _____

Her Birthday

Her birth date

_____

She likes . . .

☐ chocolate　　☐ white　　☐ marble

cake

She prefers . . .

☐ chocolate　　☐ vanilla　　☐ strawberry

ice cream

Just for Fun

Her dream vacation is . . .

☐ at the beach

☐ in the mountains

☐ in a big city

She likes travelling by . . .

☐ train   ☐ plane   ☐ car

She would rather . . .

☐ read a great book   ☐ play a game

☐ shop till she drops

About Her

She's really good at . . .

_____

She would rather win . . .

■ an Olympic medal   ■ an Academy Award

 ■ a Grammy Award

She would rather . . .

■ ride bikes   ■ in-line skate

■ ride her scooter

More Favorites

She likes . . .

- [ ] math   or   [ ] science
- [ ] Coconut   or   [ ] Licorice
- [ ] pants   or   [ ] shorts
- [ ] nighttime   or   [ ] daytime

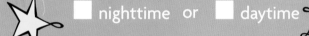 

Her favorite restaurant serves . . .

- [ ] Chinese food
- [ ] Mexican food
- [ ] Italian food

My Special Wishes for Her . . .

I Like Your Style!

Wow! I want to be singing,
My life is sure feeling great!
'Cause I learned something
    new,
Made a friend or two—
And that is something
    to celebrate!

See my sparkle,
My spirit,
My own kind of style!
Inside me I feel it
And I want to smile!

Hey! Hey! Hey!
Take a good look at me—
I'm glad to be an American girl!

Look how much I love living
At this moment in time—
I can hope, I can care,
I can shout, I can share,
And so many other choices
    are mine.

You know, because we're all
    different,
Imagine what it would be
If we each took a dream,
Went to work as a team
To make a future full
    of promise—
For you and me!

I like your sparkle,
Your spirit,
Your own special style!
Inside you, you feel it
And you want to smile!

Hey! Hey! Hey!
I think you'll agree
It's great to be an American girl!

As time goes by I know that
    things will be changing.
I wonder what I will see?
I'll make my way,
Say what I have to say,
Trying every day to be
    the best I can be!

S is Smart 'cause you excel
T—the Truth you always tell
Y—the question, You ask
L is 'cause you make me Laugh
E is for the Extra mile

Put it all together, girl,
I like your style—
I like your style!

There's a kind of a world where
    I want to live,
And there's lots of good inside
    of me I'm ready to give!
I want to fill it up with friend-
    ship, hope, and harmony—
I'm glad to be an American girl!

'Cause it's our sparkle,
Our spirit,
Our own kind of style!
Inside us, we feel it
And we want to smile!

Hey! Hey! Hey!
It's so easy to see
It's great to be an American girl!